5.00

Wimmer Lecture XX

Saint Vincent College

Latrobe, Pennsylvania

Library of Congress Cat. No. 68-29504

Nihil obstat: Francis J. Mueller
Deputatis ad hoc

Imprimatur: ✠Wm. G. Connare
Bishop of Greensburg
August 30, 1968

Scientific Indeterminism and Human Freedom

by

Henry Margenau

Wimmer Lecture XX

The Archabbey Press
Latrobe, Pennsylvania

1. Classical Determinism and its Insecurities

The physical science of the 18th and 19th centuries, often called classical science, was dominated by an overpowering belief in determinism. The laws of nature were regarded as rigid and inviolable, the course of the universe was immutably set. Man, too, was a physical system and as such subject to the inflexible laws of nature. Human freedom, on the other hand, was (for those who accepted it) a self-evident phenomenon, a mode of consciousness which declared itself as a genuine factor present in every conscious decision. Thus arose the serious problem of reconciling manifest freedom with the determinism of science.

The efforts at reconciliation fill the annals of philosophy of the last century. Roughly, they can be divided into three classes of attempts. Some thinkers, mainly scientists, tried to cut the Gordian knot by denying freedom, by declaring the overt experience of free will to be illusory and nonveridical. The second group admitted freedom as a true awareness, as a valid phase of consciousness, but regarded it as occurring only within the mind, visible through an act of introspection; when viewed externally, these philosophers felt, human actions are indeed predetermined. This view, which persists even to our day, holds freedom and determination to be complementary concepts. When man views himself introspectively he is free, but seen from the outside he is bound by laws and carried along inexorably by the cosmic process that propels him. The third school, finally, invented a variety of subterfuges to account for freedom in the face of a deterministic science. They talked about two different realms of being with laws of different kinds, or else of ignorance as beclouding the deterministic process and thereby creating

Two

the semblance of freedom. I shall say more about these endeavors at a later stage of my lecture. At this point I deem it important to present and examine the view called classical determinism, which affirms the universality of a relation called classical causality. What is this view and how did it arise?

Perhaps the clearest characterization of the state of affairs called deterministic, at any rate the one most widely quoted, is found in Laplace's famous treatise called "Analytical Theory of Probabilities", published in 1820. It reads

> An intelligence which knows at a given instant all forces acting in nature, as well as the momentary positions of all things of which the universe consists, would be able to comprehend the motions of the largest bodies of the world and those of the smallest atoms in one single formula; provided it were powerful enough to subject all data to analysis. To it, nothing would be uncertain, both future and past would be present before its eyes.

The intelligence here involved, which presumably transcends human limitations, has until recently been called a *demon*. Nowadays people tend to call it an electronic computer. Nor has the availability of such a computer-demon been drawn into question, for it was felt that its existence is quite uninteresting because it is the principle that matters: The laws of nature are in *essence* such that they permit detailed predictions—whether anybody is able to infer them or not. There is, however, one slight inaccuracy in Laplace's popular wording of his thesis, an omission which later considerations will reveal. Laplace should have added *"and velocities"* after "the position", making the clause read

> as well as the momentary positions and velocities of all things.

The basis for the dictum was the science of analytical mechanics, which had attained a highly perfect mechanical form at the hands of Newton, D'Alembert, Lagrange and Hamilton. Let me illustrate its method by ref-

erence to the simplest formulation of its principles, which is Newton's second law of motion. It asserts that the acceleration a which
results when a force F is applied to an object of mass m satisfies the relation $F = ma$.
In the simplest instance, F is a function of
the position of the mass, i.e., in one-dimen-
sional motion, $F = F(x)$. The symbol m de-
notes a constant quantity, and $a = \dfrac{d^2x}{dt^2}$.
Hence the relation, $F = ma$, represents a
second-order differential equation, indeed one
which can always be solved, even without
the aid of a demon. But as everybody with
a modest knowledge of the calculus knows,
the solution of this equation, which has the
form $x = f(t)$, contains two undetermined
constants, sometimes called constants of in-
tegration, which must be fixed before a full
solution can be written down. Their nature
is somewhat arbitrary, but their number is
not. The simplest choice is a) the position of
the mass at the initial instant and b) the

velocity of the mass at the same instant. I shall call the initial instant t_0, the initial position coordinate x_0, the corresponding velocity v_0. The solution then has the form $x = f(x_0, v_0, t)$. Furthermore, when x is known at any t, v can be obtained at once by differentiation.

So much for the mathematical situation. We now examine its wider implications. Newton discovered a law, $F = ma$. This law enables us to calculate, i.e., predict, x and v at any future time t when x_0 and v_0 are given. Because of the crucial significance of the observable quantities x and v, these two are said to form the dynamical *state* of the object whose mass is *m*. The schema of prediction may then be depicted as below. We are in possession of a fundamental law of nature,

Newton's $F = ma$. This law, which is of the mathematical form of a second order differential equation, enables us to predict, with absolute precision, the state $S(t)$ of a physical system if its state at an earlier time, $S(t_o)$, is known. The definition of a state in terms of x and v may seem artificial, but a moment's reflection shows that these are precisely the observable quantities which suffice for this definition in the following sense. They propagate themselves from present to future in a self-consistent way; no further knowledge beyond x_o and v_o is needed for a prediction of x and v at any other time; further observable quantities would not alter the prediction, and fewer would make it impossible.

It is therefore natural that physicists and mathematicians should have seized upon this mathematical concept of "state" (of a mass point); and the knowledge that there exists a law which uniquely mediates between states in time led to the formulation of the principle of causality in its modern form. Laplace's statement is a direct translation of the formal theory just sketched into philosophical terms, except for one vast extrapolation.

He assumes the universe to consist of an enormous collection of masses, each of which is subject to a law like Newton's, and he then asserts that knowledge of the present positions and velocities of *all* the particles making up the universe would in principle allow a forecast of all future states. Philosophy, as usual, adjusted itself to the science of its day or, more accurately, to the science of the preceding century and accepted the determinism which it implied. This anachronism largely persists today.

The example chosen from mechanics is not an isolated one. The schema depicted above prevailed in all of 19th century science. In every field there was a central law or set of laws. The objects controlled by these laws were described in terms of *states* which had so to speak a direct affinity to the laws: Their observables (to use a noun coined by current physics) were such that if their values were given at one time, the law would enable their calculation at any other time. States were so defined as to form suitable initial conditions for the laws of nature. One sees this in the theory of hydrodynamics, where the objects are fluid fields and the observables, pressures and flow velocities at different points within the fluid; in electrodynamics, where the object is an electromagnetic field, the observables field strengths, and the law Maxwell's equations.

It was reasonable, therefore, to believe that *every* system subject to observation is controlled by laws which admit the existence of states that propagate themselves through time in accordance with these laws, even when such systems and such states are not yet known. This belief is called determinism. The states at time t_0 are called causes, the later states at time t effects, and the formal methodological relation between them is the causal relation. Causality is the theory of this relation, often couched in less analytic and therefore vaguer terms than I have employed in its description.

It should be clear that the claim, often heard, according to which classical physical science *demonstrates* universal causality, is incorrect. The most one can say is that the procedures of physical science in earlier times *sought* to use a causal representation of events and succeeded in an amazing number of instances. Proclamation of universal causality is an extrapolation hopefully based upon this observation.

Perhaps it is well to review briefly some of the objections which can be and have been raised against Laplacian determinism. A difficulty arises from the circumstance that Laplace appeals to the entire universe in his proclamation of the causal principle. If the universe consists of a very large, perhaps even an infinite number of elementary entities[1], each subject to a law somewhat like Newton's, the feasibility of finding a solution for every x and every v, indeed the mathematical existence of such a solution, are seriously drawn into question. It may therefore be altogether idle to talk about causality in the entire physical realm. The obvious remedy for this disease is to relieve the formulation of its reference to the whole universe and to apply it to smaller systems.

This, however, can be done. Were it not for the important fact that systems, finite in extent and in the number of constituent particles (onta), are often known to have a fate which is independent of the rest of the universe, causality would be a futile subject. The availability of finite "closed systems" is a precondition for causality to be meaningful.

To be sure, completely closed systems are never found in nature and therefore display the "fictive" character of idealizations. Hence it is customary to indict the subject matter of causality and therewith causality itself as having only a spurious relevance to actual experience. But this thoughtless attitude throws out the whole of physical science by forgetting that theories never refer to the immediate directly, they always require an interposition of rules of correspondence.

All systems to which analysis can be applied are idealizations. This circumstance arises partly from the complexity and partly from what may be called the haziness of the given.[2] To admit that closed systems are idealizations does not, therefore, in the least detract from their importance, for an idealization is that toward which physical procedures *can be made to tend*, and there are ways for distinguishing proper from improper idealizations. A closed mechanical system belongs to the class of proper idealizations.

The occurrence of closed systems is by no means to be expected on a priori grounds. It is occasioned by such contingent facts as the rapid decline of all mechanical forces with increasing distance between interacting particles. Thus causality, to be valid, necessarily implies something that is far from obvious. Its implication is: *There are closed systems.*

Another objection to the doctrine of determinism comes from the camp of empiricists and positivists. They make the demon the object of controversy and wish to replace him by man, or by a scientist. Causality then becomes a question of whether the scientist, knowing the state of the universe at one time, can *in actual fact* predict it for all times. Since the answer is clearly negative, causality is said to lose its meaning. But I think that a more careful inspection of the problem removes this objection.

Laplace meant his demon to be a great mathematician, indeed one who is versed in *all* the tricks of that trade. He introduced him as an ideal arbiter of the mathematical consistency of the situation expressed in the quotation above, as one qualified to pronounce the judgment which the mathematician renders when he says: The solution of an equation exists. This judgment is meaningful even if no computer on earth has found the solution. When this interpretation is accepted, the criterion of causality is the existence of a world formula as envisioned by Laplace. And the word *existence* is to be understood in its strict mathematical sense. With this interpretation, which was clearly intended by Laplace, the lapse of the whole problem into the trivial is avoided. There are, however, more serious shortcomings of the classical deterministic view, one of which is extremely important in the context of this lecture. It concerns the meaning of the phrase: *Knowing at a given instant all forces acting in nature, as well as the momentary positions and velocities of all things.* The remainder of this section is an analysis of this clause.

There are two kinds of knowledge. One springs from definitions and is set forth in tautologies or analytic statements. Of it I can be absolutely sure. Because the atomic weight of oxygen has been defined as 16, I know its value to an infinite number of decimal places. Similarly, I know that all perfect circles are absolutely round, that the interior angles of every Euclidean triangle have a sum of exactly 180°. The other kind of knowledge is contingent or, as the philosophers say, synthetic. It has to be acquired by observation. Now there is a trait in observational knowledge which Laplace and all the scientists and mathematicians of the last century overlooked: Observable knowledge *can not* be infinitely precise.

To see this, consider the simplest kind of scientific measurement: the weighing of an object by means of a delicate balance—let alone the supermarket scale with its gross inaccuracies. Errors arise first of all because the standard weights are not perfectly calibrated, because the balance is not devoid of friction, because our judgment of coincidence between the pointer and the scale is inexact. None of these systematic limitations can be completely overcome. But even more disturbing is the fact that a measurement, made with the greatest care of which the scientist is capable, will not yield the same value on repetition. This vagary of nature, this uncertainty of the immediately given, is usually explained by invoking a myriad of minute external causes, each of which introduces its own small error into the measurement: there are air currents which offset the equilibrium of the balance, slight but variable differences in temperature which make one balance arm a little longer than the other, unseen particles of dust collecting on the pans; the keenness of the observer's attention will fluctuate. When all these small contributions to what is called the error of observation are taken into consideration a set of repeated weighings of our object must yield a dispersive set of values of well known mathematical form (a Gauss error curve), and the arithmetical mean of them is chosen as the "true" value of the weight. The scientific way of recording it, however, is to state along with the mean an estimate of the possible deviations, perhaps in the form (3.498+0.005) pounds. It is the + figure which interests us here.

Normally, it is called an error, and this carries the suggestion that man is to blame for it. A better name is "possible deviation", a term neutral enough to absolve man from culpability. The uncertainty, it will appear, is not man's fault; it is characteristic of his process of acquiring knowledge and is lodged deep in the nature of things. No conceivable —as distinct from practicable—method can eliminate it. Even Laplace's demon, the ideal mathematician, would be unable to escape it. Hence every philosopher of science must take it into account.

If it were said that omniscient God can penetrate the halo of uncertainty which surrounds every empirical observation, I would reply that this is irrelevant because omniscience makes Laplace's formula pointless and the controversy over determinism empty. The conclusion for science seems inescapable: it must reckon with the inevitability of deviations from even the most reliable values of physical observables which knowledge can reveal.

There are other respects in which the concept of absolutely certain empirical knowledge is grotesque. The coin I now place on this desk has, one would suppose, an exact position relative to the edges of the desk. More explicitly, its center, a definite point within the coin, is located above some point on the surface of the desk. To determine these points would, as we have seen, be impossible, but we can still suppose that they exist and that the coincidence is meaningful. Proceeding upon this assumption, one can then ask the question whether this coincidence can be re-established after I remove the coin from the table. I might try to put it there again, but would not succeed in hitting the exact point above which its center lay before. There is, in fact, a most rigorous theory of probability which shows that precise coincidence will *never* happen again, no matter how often I attempt to place the coin. Only if the idea of coincidence is diffused to mean coincidence within a certain area, small but finite, does the problem of replacing the coin make mathematical and physical sense.

The saving grace here lies in the phrase, small but finite. Classical physics allows one ideally to make all errors as small as he pleases. It sets no lower limit, except that of the theory's own validity. This is roughly definable as the domain of atoms. If spatial magnitudes, in our previous example the tolerance with respect to coincidence between two points, become as small as an atom, that is to say about 10^{-7} cm, all bets are off. Laplace, whose theory was classical mechanics, should have further qualified the phrase "knows the momentary positions and velocities" by adding: "within small but finite limits". But then his claim becomes erroneous, as will now be shown.

The air molecules in this room are bouncing about in random fashion, colliding with the walls and with one another. As to their positions at a given moment, let us make the severest possible assumption, namely that we know them all within a latitude of 10^{-7} cm. Every time a molecule collides with another, the "errors" of their position are compounded. Approximately, the uncertainty in our knowledge of each molecule's location is doubled in every collision. Now the number of collisions made on the average by any molecule is 10^{10} in every second. How long, then, does it take for the initial knowledge to be wiped out completely? A simple computation shows that after about 1,000 collisions our ignorance with respect to a molecule's place in this room is complete even though I know it to be within an incredibly small space at the beginning. And it takes only one ten millionth of a second for 1,000 collisions to take place and thus for the initial knowledge to perish.

The precision demanded by classical determinism is therefore self-defeating. What is

Twenty

true for the molecules in this room is true *a fortiori* for the infinitely larger number of the material constituents of the universe, with it myriads of galaxies and the innumerable brain cells of all living individuals. Nevertheless, scientific prediction retains its hold on all matters which can reasonably become objects of inquiry, and these are matters of statistics. Instead of asking: is a particular molecule within a given small volume in this room, we put the question: how many molecules are to be found within the volume or, with similar restraint: what is the probability that a given molecule will be within this volume? Interest is here transferred from precise knowledge of the properties of the individuals composing the world to a knowledge of the probabilities that they shall have these properties. These probabilities are governed by relatively simple laws of nature.

We are thus led to analyze the meaning of probability, which, as it turns out, is not unambiguous in scientific and philosophical discourse. The next section of my paper is devoted to that task. At this point, however, let me summarize what we have learned thus far. The causal relation, the concatenation of precise mechanical states or any other determinate physical conditions by equations of the Newtonian type, is self-consistent in a mathematical sense. The uncertainty inherent in all empirical knowledge, however, makes it useless and, in a physical sense, meaningless. Laplace's formula becomes inoperative, but the competence of science is restored by the introduction of probabilities. All this was seen to occur in classical physics and it makes classical determinism highly insecure. Later it will appear that the branch of modern physics called quantum mechanics deals a further, indeed a severer blow to that cherished doctrine, making it not only insecure but in principle untenable.

2. The Meaning of Probability

To many minds, probability represents a subjective index of confidence in the outcome

of an event. A wager expresses what one
believes will happen or what is true, and the
odds one is willing to accept are a numerical
measure of the intensity of one's belief. When
understood in this direct way probability becomes a quantity whose value is difficult to
specify, and it is not of great utility in any
exact science. To make such confidence in
the outcome of an event objective and quantitative, early philosophers, notably the same
Laplace whom we encountered in the preceding section, advanced this proposition:
The index of confidence equals the number of
ways in which the specific event in question
can come to pass, divided by the total number of ways in which the event can take place.
Thus, the probability of throwing a 3 with
an unbiased die is 1/6 because of the six faces
of the die which can appear uppermost only
one face carries a three. Or the chances of
drawing an ace from a deck of cards is 1/13
because there are four aces and 52 cards. Just
why this ratio should determine odds is not

logically clear, but it seems reasonable that one should pay $1.00 for a gain of $6.00 in case a specified number, like 3, is thrown with a good die.

This definition of probability, which takes it to be the ratio of the number of favorable events to the total number of possible events, is often called an *a priori* definition, since it allows a calculation of probabilities before any event has actually happened. When carefully inspected it is not as simple as might at first appear. For while the nature of the favorable event is usually well conceived, the total number of possible events often suffers from lack of precision. The die might, by accident, be caught in a crack of the table and expose an edge rather than a face. A simple redefinition ruling out this contingency will set matters aright in that instance, but what does one do when the die is loaded? It still has 6 faces, yet the ratio 1/6 needs to be modified. To take care of such irregularities Laplace found it necessary to define probability as the ratio of the number of favorable events to the number of *equipossible* events. Clearly, this begs the question, for the word equipossible must really be interpreted as equiprobable, and then the definition is circular.

Interesting proposals have been made to remove these difficulties. One is an appeal to ignorance: Instances or cases must be regarded as equiprobable if *no reason can be given* for assuming one to be more probable than another. This takes care of the die if I know it to be loaded. But what about the probability that a complete stranger whom I meet is a thief? The alternative is clear; he is either a thief or he is not, and since I know nothing about him I must judge the probability that he is a thief to be 1/2. —Finally there are situations where not even the principle of ignorance succeeds in establishing a numerical value, as for instance in the calculation of the probability of death of an individual. Certainly this cannot be taken to be the ratio of all possibilities of dying to all possibilities of remaining alive and of dying. It becomes evident, therefore, that the a priori probability needs somehow to be augmented and stabilized by another concept, more thoroughly grounded in observations and useful in *testing* the values which Laplace's ratio assigns.

Here enters the idea of probability as a frequency of occurrences, to be ascertained not merely by thinking about possible events but by experimenting with them. We actually throw the die in anticipation of our bet and find that in 100 throws the three appears 18 times; in the next 100 throws it comes up 16 times, and so on. We may then take the relative frequency, the number of favorable occurrences (appearance of a 3) divided by the total number of throws, to be a measure of the probability. This procedure is demanded by the frequency theory, or the frequency definition, of probability. It is clearly an *a posteriori* formulation of this concept, for it depends upon experimentation and can only be established after numberous trials. Its advantages are great; it removes all the difficulties that attended the *a priori* approach. The hypothesis of ignorance is no longer necessary; there is no trouble with a loaded die, and the actuarial use of probabilities is reasonably accounted for: The probability of death of an individual in a specified age group is simply the number of people in a similar group who die (within a stated time) divided by the total number of people in his group.

However, the frequency theory introduces a few difficulties of its own. The first one arises when one attempts to make the number representing the probability precise. In an example of the die, is it 0.18 or 0.16? It was believed at one time that the reason for this variation in the ratio lay in the insufficiency of our sample, the mere 100 throws. If we consider the two series as one, take the number of threes to be $18 + 16$ and the number tosses to be 200, we obtain $p = 0.17$.

The suggestion is that by making the series infinite and counting favorable events we shall get an exact and unique value for the probability. This, unfortunately, is not the case, for it may be shown that a mathematical limit of the relative frequency as the number of events increases without limit does not exist, at least not in the ordinary sense of a limit. Some thinkers of the past have regarded this misfortune as a reason for rejecting the idea of probability as a frequency, but the power of their arguments has diminished since mathematicians have been able to redefine the limit concept in a new way so as to make it applicable to relative frequencies.

One feature of the a posteriori formulation which, I believe, can not be erased or composed by redefinition is its failure to be applicable to single events, that is to say to events which can not be repeated. Ensembles, assemblages of numerous cases must be available for its proper determination and for its interpretation. From this it follows that a person who rejects every a priori approach to probability has no basis for arguing about the probability or improbability of the creation of our universe, or about the probability or improbability of its annihilation, or about the origin of life. For these are single events which cannot be regarded as parts of ensembles. Failure to heed this caveat has made many scientific pronouncements on such matters indefensible.

Although it should be apparent from the foregoing discussion, let me emphasize the fact that the two probability conceptions, a priori ratio and relative frequency, are logically different. By no device of reason is it possible to show that the exact ratio 1/6 of the number of *faces* of a die with a 3 on them to the total number of *faces*, has anything to do with the discussed ratio of *throws*. The fact that the latter also yields a number near 1/6 is, logically speaking, a miracle. The relation we encounter here is one that troubled

Plato; it is the relation of thought to fact, and it needs careful consideration. First, however, I wish to take the problem out of the narrow context in which my desire for simple exposition has placed it. And to avoid circumlocution I shall use a novel terminology which our language (in contrast to others) permits and refer to a priori probability as *likelihood*, to the concept based on frequencies as probability. This usage is suggested by the etymology of the word probable, which means provable, testable by empirical means.

The concept of likelihood need not take the Laplacean form. Its only condition is that there shall be some theory which allows it to be formed in advance of actual observation. The theory may have been suggested, or even tested, by earlier experimentation (as was Laplace's likelihood), but it must not speak of frequencies. For instance, the molecular theory of physics says that the probability of our finding a given N_2 molecule of this room within the space now enclosed by my hand is the volume of that space divided by the volume of this room. Another theory enables one to calculate the likelihood that light shall be emitted by an atom, another the likelihood that it will rain when certain clouds are formed. Strictly, all these are a priori versions of probability, i.e. likelihoods, which have intrinsically nothing to do with the number of times the events concerned will happen.

A posteriori probability formulations, which test these likelihoods, are not as numerous. Observation of frequencies is by far most common in science. The assertion that likelihoods *must* be confirmed as frequencies and nothing else is not uncommon. One might suggest, however, that there are other operational tests. In the life insurance business, the financial break-even point is the one that validates computed likelihoods. Roulette players recognize sooner or later, when they continue to win or lose, whether their chances have been estimated correctly. By and large, however, frequencies of occurrence—to which these other criteria can ultimately be reduced, are the principal *a posteriori* or empirical meanings of probability.

We now confront the miracle: Why do the logically unrelated, computed likelihoods agree numerically with the probabilities? The pragmatist has a simple answer: if they did not, they would be rejected. This is certainly true but not very revealing, for it enjoins on us an attitude of nil mirari which fails to wonder about the curious fact that so simple a concept as the Laplacian ratio should have relevance for our complicated world. The issue we are facing here is wide, indeed it encompasses all of science.

Every measurable scientific quantity partakes of the logical duality exhibited by the likelihood-probability relation. As an example, consider temperature. One definition, the operational one, identifies it with a number which marks the coincidence between the top of a mercury column and a scale. Another takes it to be, in certain units, the mean kinetic energy of the molecules of a substance. One of these is not logically entailed by the other. Or consider the meaning of force. It is something which can be read from the dial of a dynomometer, and it is also mass times acceleration. Or take a concept like time. It is a quantity indicated numerically by a clock; it is also that elusive thing which troubled St. Augustine and is sometimes vaguely defined as the independent variable in the laws of mechanics, or as distance divided by speed in uniform motion. The point is that a scientific observable, to be completely useful, must be understood in two different ways, one referring to direct experience, the other to related theoretical constructs. Hence it must possess two different kinds of definition, one operational or "epistemic", the other constitutive in the sense that the non-operational meaning of the term is constituted or established, as it were, by relations to other concepts. An operational definition of force is in terms of dynamometer readings, a constitutive one specifies it to be mass times acceleration. By virtue of the first the scientist is able to measure, by virtue of the second he can reason about forces.

Most scientific quantities permit a plethora of definitions, some of which are epistemic, some constitutive. There occurs an interplay between them; constitutive definitions are sometimes converted to, or viewed as, laws of nature, and that operational definition which conforms to the simplest or the most general law is ultimately adopted. It would, I think, be fascinating and informative to write a history of science from the point of view of the feedback between operational and constitutive definitions of scientific quantities. So far, to my knowledge, this has not been done.

On the other hand, quantities like the id of some psychiatrists, which, as I understand it, can not be defined epistemically, or a negative probability which also lacks an operational definition, are of no interest in science. Neither is at present a concept like intelligence which, although it enjoys numerous operational definitions, (intelligence tests), does not embed itself in a reasonable psychological theory which links it with other characteristics of man. There is no good way to reason about it because of the absence—so far as I can see—of an adequate constitutive definition. The lesson is simple: every quantitative scientific concept, to be fully formed, must have both a constitutive and an epistemic definition.

A scientific theory contains statements which *equate* the two definitions, and such an equation functions as a law of nature. Newton's law says in effect that a force F, measurable by virtue of its operational definition, is also equal to mass m times acceleration a. Each of the two quantities, m and a, also has an operational definition, so that the relation,

F = ma, can be empirically tested. Temperature T, measured by means of a thermometer, is testable through the constitutive relation pV = RT, where p is pressure and V the volume of a gas, each operationally definable. The theoretical relation, pV = RT, which serves as a constitutive definition of T, can be derived from other, more basic propositions, such as the statement that T is the mean kinetic energy of molecules. These simple instances are typical of the whole of science.

Now we turn again to probability. Laplace's rule, indeed every theoretical concept of likelihood, functions as the constitutive definition of probability, the operational frequency concept allows it to be tested. If the test is successful, then equating Laplace's ratio, favorable to total number of possibilities, to the frequency-of-occurrence ratio sets forth a law of nature. That it should be valid is no more and no less astonishing than that a formula like F = ma should be true in the world.

This is not the occasion to probe more deeply into the reasons for the adequacy of simple laws to our complex universe, a matter which has been discussed at length elsewhere.[1] What I wish you to recognize is that the concept of probability exhibits all the normal features of measurable scientific quantities and enters, even in the simplest scientific situations, into the formulation of the laws of nature. For certain reasons, this is not generally acknowledged. It is felt that probability is somehow not a respectable scientific term, that it appears only in an incompletely analyzed physical situation, that he who invokes it confesses ignorance. Because of its singular status, probability has been regarded in ways wholly different from other scientific observables; in particular, its different definitions have been considered as contradictory. Two schools of thought came into being, the *a priorists* and the *frequentists*, each arguing for the virtues of its cherished definition. The foregoing development was intended to prove: 1) that the two kinds of definitions are not contradictory but complementary, as they are in all similar instances, and 2) that by this very token probability is a physical quantity which fully merits a role in the fundamental laws of nature.

Let me attempt to remove one final misconception. It is said that probability can not be a good and measurable attribute of scientific objects because its value cannot be determined in one fell swoop. Its operational definition involves a very large number of observations, whereas the ascertainment of a normal quantity, like the length of this room, requires a single measuring act. This, however, is a naive contention, partly true because one is ordinarily not interested in a very accurate value of the length. If it were required to be known to 1/1000 of an inch, as might be true in some modern experiments, a single observation would not suffice; one would carry out a large number of measurements and consider their statistical fluctuations. In a word, one would proceed much in the way in which one measures probabilities.

To sum up our results in terms of an example, again the much belabored die: This physical object has a great variety of scientific observables, among them its position, size, its shape, its weight, its color, but also the probability of falling 3 uppermost and all the other probabilities. We shall see in the next section that in the realm of atomic objects, physical entities may actually lose some of these "obvious" observables, such as color and position, while retaining probabilities.

3. Probabilities in Quantum Mechanics

Perhaps it is desirable to demonstrate with reference to a few specific examples how so radical a change in the physicist's view of nature could come to pass. First, then, let me recall what difference the size of an object can make in our basic conception of it.

Imagine a spherical object, say a blue billiard ball. Its obvious observables are color, shape, size, position in space, velocity, etc. We shall assume it to be at rest. Our imagination does not prevent us from conceiving the ball as an indefinitely small sphere, and we tend to think of all the foregoing observables as clinging to it regardless of its size. But suppose its size is diminished 100 fold, so that the ball is barely visible. Is it still blue, round, at rest, etc.? Yes, because a simple magnifying glass restores all these qualities to our perception. Now let us shrink it some more, by another factor 100. The object is no longer visible, but every doubt as to its visual qualities can be removed by viewing it under a microscope of high resolution. It will no longer be at rest; the air molecules impinge on it to make it perform Brownian motion— but it is still spherical, blue, and of definite size. Thus we are prone to conclude that objects of all sizes have these descriptive properties; we glide into the facile belief that the qualities of the macrocosm are found reproduced in the microcosm.

To see how false this is we need only re-
duce the size of the ball further. Another
factor of one thousand will bring it down to
the size of a large molecule. It now begins to
leave its color behind, for it is smaller than a
wave length of light and can no longer be
blue. Assignment of color to it becomes *meaningless*. Still further reduction in size raises
serious problems about its location in space.
Signals designed to "find" it, present a para-
dox. If they are of small enough wave length
to be reflected by it they will knock it away
in an unforseeable manner, if they are chosen
to affect it gently and without disturbance
their waves are so long as to pass over it
without yielding a record of the particle's position. Size and shape are similarly affected.
Here, then, are a few indications to suggest
that very small things may require a new
kind of description that is different from the
customary assignment of visual attributes.

Further insight is offered by an old atomic

theory, that of Bohr, and its most interesting failures. It proposed a planetary model of the hydrogen atom, with the proton at its center forming the (nearly) stationary sun and the light-weight electron revolving about it in some specified stationary orbit. All properties of the system were calculable from the basic laws of mechanics and electromagnetism, and the consequences to which they led, in particular regarding the frequencies of the lines in the H-spectrum, were beautifully verified in observations. Rarely did a model satisfy the scientists' craving for understanding and predicting as thoroughly as did Bohr's picture.

Hence there was consternation when it failed, failed not so much in the domain of observations but by implying things which were useless and contradictory in a basic theoretical sense. They were useless because some features of the model were incapable of being observed, and scientists do not operate with concepts which have no operational counterparts. They were contradictory because some of the implications could not be simultaneously true, to wit:

Bohr's model, in assuming the electron to pursue a path around the proton, assigned to it a definite place in space at any given time. The electron's speed of revolution, when calculated in accordance with Bohr's assumptions, is such that it revolves about 10^{16} times in one second. Despite this terrific speed, the electron's "position at an instant" was thought to be meaningful because it could be measured by allowing a signal, e.g. a gamma ray, to be reflected from it while it was revolving. The direction of the reflected ray would then allow an inference as to the electron's position. To be sure, an experiment of this kind could hardly be performed upon a single electron in an atom, but as a "thought experiment"—and atomic physics bristles with thought experiments—it seemed to provide a perfectly meaningful method for determining the electron's position.

Yet a simple consideration invalidates it altogether. For by the laws of electromagnetism on which Bohr's model is in part founded, a certain time interval is required if an electromagnetic signal like a gamma ray is to be reflected by a charged particle, and this interval, the time during which the photon and the electron are in collusion, turns out to be of the order of 10^{-9} sec. Where, then, was the electron at the time of reflection? The answer is: anywhere in its orbit, for it revolved a million times during this "position measurement". Thus, when the Bohr model suggested that the electron should have a measurable position and at the same time that the position cannot be measured, it contradicted itself.

The brief sketch here given is not wholly convincing, for it leaves open the possibilities that a) there may be other ways in which the electron's position can in fact be determined at every instant or b) the electron *has* a position even though it is not accessible to measurement. The facts, however, are that possibility a) has been virtually ruled out because an exhaustive search has failed to reveal such ways, and possibility b) is abandoned by most scientists for a reason that is important relative to an understanding of modern science and sets it apart from other disciplines, such as speculative philosophy and religion: science will not operate with concepts that are wholly barred to observation and measurement.

Let me now describe a feasible experiment which allows a consistent inference with respect to the electron's place. It is one in which many photons, e.g. X-rays, are reflected from many atoms in one collective act. One then finds that the reflected rays form a diffraction pattern which suggests that the electrons were in all sorts of places, mostly on or near their respective Bohr orbits. If a pattern were drawn in which the density of shading indicates the likelihood that an electron might be found at a place in question, a diagram like Figure 1 would

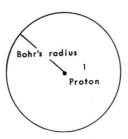

Figure 1

result. The Bohr orbit marks indeed the most probable locus of all electrons, each with respect to its own proton. Yet many can be found some distance away from this "normal" path, quite in contrast with Bohr's visual scheme.

Again, what interests the physicists is no longer the electron's path, its precise location in space. In fact most of them deny that it has a path, deny that its motion can be visualized at all. They take seriously the density smear of Figure 1 which, in mathematical parlance, is a probability. The quantum theory, which was designed for our understanding and predicting the behavior of electrons, no longer speaks of their instantaneous position but only of their place probabilities. And this theory has been so successful that the Bohr model, now regarded as false, is taught today only as a qualitative, stepping stone to the more adequate theory. Some say that this theory also represents a model, but a model which is no longer mechanistic or pictorable to the mind's eye. It is a probabilistic, or a mathematical model, more modest in its claim to visual understanding but fruitful in the extreme, for everything it says about atomic electrons is verifiably correct.

In the new theory, called quantum mechanics, probabilities play a most extensive and a most fundamental role. They are ultimates, appearing in the prime formulation of the laws of nature. They are not reducible to certainties even theoretically, even though this was essentially true about the probabilities in statistical mechanics. The smear of Figure 1 takes the place of a *state* ($x_1 v_1$ of an electron) in Newton's mechanics, and the causal laws (Schrödinger's or Dirac's) relate the smear corresponding to an atomic antity at time t_0 to another one at a later time t. More exactly, the state in quantum mechanics is a vector in Hilbert space, e.g. a state function ψ, whose *square* is the probability of position. This technicality, however, need not detain us here.

The behavior of all states, and hence all probabilities in quantum mechanics is controlled by the indeterminacy principle of Heisenberg. Elementary texts often introduce this basic law by considering how one kind of measurement interferes with another, using the familiar concepts of ordinary physics. This leads to a woeful misunderstanding of the principle, making it appear as a sort of practical limitation on measuring procedures and masking its true significance. Let me present it here in a less obvious but more meaningful way, even at the risk of being a little formal.

Suppose I say that an electron is in a state for which the probability of position is $ce^{-(\frac{x}{a})^2}$. This is a Gaussian curve of width d. Physically, it means that the electron has been shot from an electron gun with a certain arrangement of accelerating disks and diaphragms. To test the correctness of the probability function, $ce^{-(\frac{x}{a})^2}$, one can proceed in one of two ways. One sets up a sensitive plate at right angles in front of the gun and allows the electron to impinge on it, leaving a blackened mark where it strikes. The electron is then reprepared, i.e. it, or another one—for all electrons are known to have the same elementary properties—is sent through the gun under the same conditions and its impact on the plate is noted. This is done a great number of times, so that the plate is continuously but not uniformly blackened, the darkest places being those at which the greatest number of electrons struck. The state of the electrons is the one we have assumed if the blackening, which is a measure of the relative frequency of impacts, is given by the formula $ce^{-\left(\frac{x}{a}\right)^2}$.

The same result could be obtained if many electrons were sent through the gun simultaneously. The blackened pattern would then result at once. This procedure is indeed the one most likely to be used by physicists, but I prefer here the foregoing test because it shows that the probability is somehow built into *each electron* as it leaves the gun.

The blackened smear might look like Figure 2. The probability distribution, $W(x)$,

Figure 2

is plotted in Figure 3. That curve is somehow

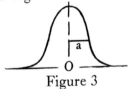

Figure 3

characteristic of each electron shot out of the gun, not only of the swarm.

As each of them leaves the gun, other measurements can be made upon it. One might, for example, send it through a magnetic field and determine its momentum in the x-direction from the curvature of its path. What one finds is this. All electrons have different momenta p, but if a histogram is made, that is to say if the number of individuals have a given p is plotted against p, a curve like Figure 4 results. Its mathematical

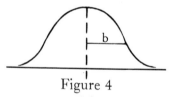

Figure 4

form is $W(p) = de^{-(\frac{p}{b})^2}$. Now the quantum theory makes a strange prediction: if Figure 3 is narrow, Figure 4 is wide, and vice versa. One can not make both indefinitely narrow. The spread of the probabilities is correlated. And this result is verified in observations.

It is possible by means of a suitable arrangement of slits in the gun to contract W(x) into a vertical line at 0. This means its position is known precisely, the value of a is zero. It then turns out that the W(p) curve is infinitely broad; nothing at all can be known about the individual momenta. Mathematically then $b \longrightarrow \infty$. There is no way of preventing this. It will be noticed that a and b are measures of the dispersions of the W(x) and W(p) curves, they are indices of "uncertainty" with respect to position and momentum.

Heisenberg's famous indeterminacy principle affirms that $ab = \frac{h}{2\pi}$. It is customary to denote a, the "uncertainty" of position, by Δx, and b by Δp. Hence

$$\Delta x \cdot \Delta p = \frac{h}{2\pi}$$

where h is Planck's constant.

Our choice of $W(x) = ce^{-\left(\frac{x}{a}\right)^2}$ was a very special one. It happens to produce minimum uncertainty. Had we chosen any other form for $W(x)$, as could be done by altering the conditions in the gun, the right hand side of the foregoing equation would have been larger. Hence, in general,[4]

$$\Delta x \cdot \Delta P \geqslant \frac{h}{2\pi}$$

Onta very often appears in states of known momentum. In that case, no device of science can ascertain where they are or where they will collide with a given object. Their place of incidence is not subject to causal determination. Classical determinism, weakened already by such considerations as were presented in section 1, has now broken down completely.

4. Ethics and Science

The title of this lecture seems to link together two basic but evidently quite disparate disciplines: science and ethics. The question as to the relationship between them can thus hardly be avoided. In my book[5], "Ethics and Science", this subject is treated at length. Present circumstances force me to be brief and suggest a compromise. In this lecture I shall present only those aspects of the larger problems in the no-man's land between the two fields which have an immediate bearing on freedom or are necessary for a proper understanding of what follows, but an appendix added to the published lecture is to provide some of the details that are here omitted.

First of all, one must give up the simple minded view that science deals with facts and ethics with values, and that the twain, facts and values, will never meet. Such a characterization recalls the comment of a young student who first met the subjects of physics and chemistry. He thought they were completely different on the basis of their definitions: When it pops it's physics; when it smells it's chemistry—and smells are different from noises. No, the classification in terms of values in the present instance will not do; even the most cursory inspection will show that ethics abounds with behavioral facts and science with personal preferences and values.

What is important, however, is the crucial occurrence of a special class of values in ethics. In the appendix I have called them *esto* values to distinguish them from factual, or *est* values. The latter are abstractions from the de facto behavior of people, descriptive of the way, good or bad, in which they happen to act. Above them is the level of the ought, the *esto*, the level of normative precepts in terms of which the goodness of *est* values can be judged. "Thou shalt" is the phrase introducing an ought, de facto values are stated in descriptive sentences.

Confusion between the is and the ought amounts to more than a philosophical error; in our day and our society it almost constitutes a cultural tragedy. Misguided prophets among our sociologists, psychiatrists and lawyers deliberately equate what is done by the majority to the ethically good, confusing mores and ethics. More and more we find crime condoned because of its widespread practice; sins become consequences of environment, conscience a hangover from earlier unenlightened tribal experiences, impressed on our minds by unreasoning fear. The clarion call of the ought is lost in the clamor of voices describing what people do; Kinsey reports are endowed with the authority of ethical codes.

Returning to our primary theme, I recall that *est* values belong to the realm of science; anthropology and sociology are full of them. Esto values, their formulation, explication and forceful conveyance to individual minds are the province of ethics. How they are established is considered in the appendix. They do not come from science. The independence of ethics from science has been recognized in the earliest days of Western philosophy. Its classical affirmation is found in Plato's Phaido (98 C ff) and Aristotle spoke of the transition from the physical to the moral sphere as a "metabasis eis allo genos", a passage into another realm. This transcendence is not questioned here. However science, through its methodology, provides hints for the understanding of ethical norms. For there are two philosophic problems which extend along parallel lines, one scientific the other ethical. The scientific one concerns the way in which our mind ascends from the particularity and flux of finite observations to knowledge of universal laws. The ethical one is connected with a formally similar rise from actual behavior to esto norms. Science has solved its problem in a reasonably competent manner, and its logic, if not its facts, should be of interest to the moral philosopher.

But the crucial quality of the ought is this: it engages man's free response and his responsibility. An esto value implies freedom of choice, for man is not like Augustine's angels who are constrained to act in accord with divine commands. Remember his simple lines: Angelus non potest peccare; homo potest non peccare. Or the biblical phrase made memorable by Steinbeck's novel: Timshel, thou mayest. This is where the problem of freedom, with the background of modern science which qualifies it, impinges on the fundamental concerns of ethics.

5. *Human Freedom*

In the first three sections of this lecture I have sketched the determinism of classical physics and the indeterminism of present science. The latter was not recognized until the present century. The problem of freedom, however, has been with us since the dawn of philosophy, and it behooves us now to follow up the allusions at the beginning of section 1 and comment on the uneasy union between deterministic science and freedom-conscious moral philosophy which existed throughout the centuries that preceded ours.

A systematic review of all the devices whereby philosophers have tried to harmonize causality and freedom is impossible here. A sketch of three of them must suffice. One, which has the authority of Spinoza and some

modern theologians, invokes a distinction between inward and outward experiences. Freedom is a phenomenon of consciousness of
which one becomes aware by introspection.
Determinism regulates processes from without. A stone in flight, said Spinoza, if it were
awakened to consciousness, would deem itself to move along its predetermined path;
it would feel it had chosen its trajectory.
The difference between determinism and
freedom has been likened to two seemingly
contradictory properties of physical objects:
The windshield of a car is concave when seen
from the inside, convex from the outside.
This explanation, in spite of its allegorical
appeal, nevertheless leaves freedom in an unsatisfactory state, for when all is said and
done it remains a psychological illusion.

Next is a thesis which accounts for freedom
by an appeal to ignorance. An omniscient
being is not free, since knowing what happens
excludes all choice in situations which other-
wise permit it. The example sometimes cited

is that of a child which is given a choice between a dish of spinach and a piece of pie. His mother, knowing that he dislikes spinach, knows the outcome, concludes therefore that he has no choice, while the child believes he is facing a genuine alternative. It is the limitation of his knowledge about himself which gives him the sense of being free. Again, it is difficult to see how this kind of reasoning explains any more than one's *feeling* of freedom, not its actual existence.

Last is a view which is found in the writings of Kant and developed in detail to fit modern science by Cassirer. Their philosophy, called transcendental idealism, regards causality as a category of human understanding, a necessary form in which all knowledge of events must be cast. For things in themselves, which lie beyond our comprehension, causality and all other basic modes of thought are irrelevant. This is what is meant by calling causality a transcendental principle of understanding. From this point of view universal causality or determinism, whether of the classical or the quantum mechanical sort, must not be regarded as a metaphysical constraint upon all forms of being. It must be distinguished from what Cassirer calls a "dinglicher Zwang". Freedom, too, is a transcendental principle, but one regulating our actions, and it therefore controls another realm. If both were factual, descriptive attributes of the world they would indeed collide; only their transcendental nature keeps them out of conflict and makes them compatible.

Now it seems to me that classical determinism and freedom do collide—in a factual sense if both are taken as ultimate metaphysical principles, and in the form of logical irreconcilables if they are transcendental modes of explanation which regulate our understanding. Let me illustrate the meaning of this claim by reference to a trivial example (which has no ethical significance, to be sure).

Suppose I am asked to raise my hand, I

can do this mechanically without thought and without engaging my will. In that case, habit acquired during my student days will probably cause me to raise my right hand. One may look upon this action as a causal one, whose result is predictable in terms of conditions existing in my brain, of associations acquired, of neural pathways previously established, and so on. But notice: I took care to say that I would *probably* raise my right hand, thereby implying something less than strict predictability.

But if I am told: raise which ever hand you wish, the sequence of events is different. I am somehow challenged to think and then to make a choice. To believe that, during the moment of reflection preceding the decision to raise my left hand, the configuration of the molecules in my body, the currents in my brain cells, or even the psychological variables composing my mental state have already predetermined that I must raise my left hand is clearly false, for it contradicts the most elementary, the most reliable, self-declarative awareness of choice which accompanies this act.[6] Thus a serious contradiction arises if strict causality is a metaphysical fact.

Nor can the situation be saved by saying, with Kant and Cassirer, that causality is merely a transcendental principle in terms of which we are required to conceive things. For in that case we should require *one* principle of understanding to comprehend the sequence of events which compose the objective course leading to the raising of my left hand, and a different, incompatible one to explain my feeling of freedom. Human reason does not tolerate two incoherent principles where a single one will do. I shall now show that the loosening of causality required by quantum mechanics enlarges the scope of that principle sufficiently to allow removal of these difficulties and to cover both determination and freedom.

What I hope to accomplish needs careful

statement. It might seem to be a proof that quantum mechanics has solved the problem of freedom. This is a vastly different task from showing that quantum mechanics has removed an essential obstacle from the road toward its solution, while the problem remains unsolved in its major details. The following analysis is directed toward this latter, much more modest aim. In approaching it, however, many of the difficulties, whose resolution constitutes the difference between the first and second tasks, will move into view.

The decision which hand to raise is totally without ethical relevance; it merely illustrates the contrast between instinctive-reflexive, almost mechanical behavior and an action which involves thought and will, thereby engaging to a small extent the quality of freedom. The question of motivation, so essential in ethics, hardly enters at all. Or if it does, if for some conscious reason—perhaps the desire to surprise my partner—I have chosen to lift my left arm when he expected the right one to be raised, that reason is far from the concerns of ethics. The distance from here to choices which can be said to be *morally* good or bad, which conform or do not conform to ethical principles, which carry responsibility, is very great. Yet somehow it can be travelled by vehicles already at our disposal. Most theories of ethics, including the one outlined in section 4, achieve their end, the explanation of moral behavior, *once the possibility of freedom and motivation is established*. These qualities, however, are present at least in embryonic form in the example we chose for discussion; hence we return to it. Its relative simplicity is an important advantage.

Precisely what happened to me as a conscious person during that crucial interval in which I "made up my mind" to raise my left hand? Of the enormous variety of physical and chemical processes which took place in my body I am not aware. I do know, however, that the physical condition before the arm raising and that after the act were connected by a continuous series of objective physical happenings. And the entire series could have been different because of my will, because of a choice of physical possibilities that were open to me.

The mental processes during the crucial interval are likewise difficult to record in detail. Nevertheless the following is perfectly clear. I was aware of having a choice, there was a moment of reflection, perhaps a brief recall of past occasions, then came a glimmer of rudimentary satisfaction in doing the unexpected, next a decision and finally the act. The choice was enacted within consciousness, and it evidently was permitted, but merely permitted, by the physical processes that took place.

One thing, then, is utterly apparent: freedom is not wholly a problem of physical science but one involving biology, physiology and psychology as well. Upon realizing this one immediately confronts the standard ques-

tion of *reducibility*: Are the laws of psycho-
physiology merely elaborate versions of those
encountered in the physico-chemical world,
or do they differ radically? The first alternative which assumes the possibility of reduc-
ing all behavior to physico-chemical bases
need not be tied to the naive supposition that
all the laws of these basic sciences are now
known, and it will not be construed in this
narrow sense here. The second, which main-
tains a radical difference, takes two essential
forms. First, one may interpret the difference
as mere transcendence, secondly as outright
violation of physico-chemical laws.

To avoid circumlocutions, let us refer to
the first alternative, that of reducibility, as I.
The second will be labelled II, and we shall
designate transcendence by IIa, violation by
IIb. As already mentioned, acceptance of I
does not commit us to the view that all basic
laws of nature are already known.

The precise meaning of IIa involves a
theory of levels of complexity among physical

phenomena. It is most simply illustrated by recalling the relation between the mechanics of point masses and the statistical mechanics of gases which are here viewed as large assemblages of molecules, in the form of point masses. To describe the mechanical state of each individual molecule one needs to specify its position and its velocity, nothing more. The totality of molecules, the gas, however, exhibits measurable properties like pressure, temperature and entropy which have no meaning with respect to single molecules. In this sense they are radically different from the properties of point masses. Yet if the positions and velocities of all molecules were known, the aggregate observables, i.e. pressure, temperature and entropy, could be calculated. These latter characterize a level of complexity *above* the mechanics of mass points. Explanation is continuous from below; the concepts of the lower level have meaning on the upper, but not the reverse.

It is seen, therefore, that thesis IIa asserts

no incompatibility between concepts and principles on two different levels. The physico-chemical and the physio-psychological can probably be regarded in a similar way as two different levels of complexity, even though the differences are so great that the full connection is not at present in evidence. The view, however, seems reasonable. If it is accepted, and the gap can some day be filled, the higher level concepts can be reached from below and thus be reduced.

The bearing of alternative IIa upon the problem of freedom, which as we have seen is encountered in the upper realm, is now apparent. Freedom cannot appear in the domains of physiology and psychology if indeterminacy is not already lodged in physics. Strict causality among the molecules, applied upward as a principle of nature to explain the behavior of aggregates, cannot entail freedom because of the requirement of continuity from below. It is equally impossible to engender freedom in the realm of psychology when strict determinism rules physics, so long as hypothesis IIa is maintained.

For our present purpose, therefore, IIa can be identified with I: neither permits freedom unless strict determinism is abandoned in physics.

Only alternative IIb provides the possibility of freedom in the face of unrelieved classical causality as it is understood in pre-quantum physics. That view cannot be rejected out of hand; indeed it is very prevalent. Since it is forced to assume the occurrence of violations of the normal order of nature, it is tantamount to a belief in miracles. As for myself, I refuse to regard freedom as a miracle so long as other avenues of explanation are open. This is the case if alternative I or IIa is adopted, *provided physical indeterminacy is taken seriously*.

I judge IIa to be the safest hypothesis, and propose to describe its consequences. This is a somewhat unpopular course; it forces us to part company with many distinguished moral philosophers who see the autonomy of ethics threatened when a relation of any sort is assumed to exist between that august discipline and science. For centuries, humanists have been impressed by the slogan already discredited in section 4 of this lecture, that science deals with facts, ethics with values, and these two categories are so disparate that they must forever stand apart. If unanalyzed this is a foolish and a dangerous dogma. Some feel that a view which finds a root of freedom in physical science denigrates and demeans the high estate of ethics whose legitimate concerns should not seek refuge in the indeterminacies of natural events. Ethics, says Cassirer, should not be forced to build its nests in the gaps of physical causation, but he fails to tell where else it should build them, if at all.

The view proposed here can hardly be criticised as debasing ethics, or as depriving it of autonomy. For in the first place, if, in espousing indeterminacy, physics abdicates control over part of its former domain, entrusting it to other hands, it does not threaten ethics. The new mood of physics is not one of intransigeance but of renunciation. Secondly, embracing the belief that freedom is made possible by indeterminacies in nature will not *solve* the problem of freedom. As will appear later, it permits only one first step towards its solution, but an important step to a place from which freedom can be seen as a scientific challenge, where it appears no longer as a fallacy or an illusion. Beyond it lies an open countryside in which ethics must travel without the guidance of science if it wishes to explore the meaning of good and bad, the origin of moral values—in short if it wishes to convert the offer of science, which might be named *chance*, into responsible *choice*.

Another consideration must be borne in mind. Throughout this lecture one single physical law is continually called upon to do extremely heavy duty, namely Heisenberg's indeterminacy principle. It is unreasonable to suppose that this item of knowledge is absolute in its present understanding, forever immune to reformulation and refinement. Future discoveries will doubtless place it in a new light, but it is difficult to see how its essence, which is drawn upon in the present context, can ever be relinquished. No one, of course, can rule out this possibility. But it seems far more likely, and here is where I would place my bet, that further principles even more widely restrictive of Laplacian causality will enter science, in which case the position here taken will be re-enforced.

Quantum indeterminacy, being the only item of its kind now firmly known, must thus be placed in the center of the present discussion. Also, the time has come to be specific. An important argument has been directed against the use to which that principle is here to be put, namely the argument which asserts that indeterminacy is limited to the atomic realm and loses its validity in the macrocosm.

Its importance in atomic and subatomic phenomena is crucial, for without it the behavior of elementary particles makes no sense. But a complex organ like the human brain, the cortex, even a brain cell or a neuron consist of vast numbers of elementary particles, and it is well known that the statistics of large numbers usually add up to certainties. While the motion of a single molecule in a gas must be specified with wide margins of probabilities, the entire gas behaves in predictable fashion. Insurance companies can only assign a probability to the occurrence of death in a given period for a specific individual, but they are almost certain of the number of deaths in a large group of people. So, too, it can be argued that the organic structures which carry the physical function of free decision are predictable in their total action even in view of elementary uncertainty; in other words, that the indeterminacy of atomic events is ironed out in the macrocosm. The assertion is respectable, for since we do not understand the function of physiological complexes in terms of atomic processes it can not be disproved.

Another, slightly different consideration, leads to the same result. If the principle of indeterminacy is written for position (x) and velocities (v) it reads

$$\Delta x \cdot \Delta v \geqslant \frac{h}{2m}$$

m being the mass of the object whose motion is being studied. Now for an electron the quantity on the right of this inequality is about 1 (in c.g.s. units). Hence if we assume its position to be wholly uncertain within the volume of the atom, where it usually resides, and assign to Δx the value 10^{-8} cm (size of an atom), Δv must be about 10^8 cm/sec; the *indeterminacy* in velocity amounts to more than 100 times the speed of an I.C.B.M. Many unforeseeable things can happen within that range of ignorance.

For a brain cell, m is at least one trillion

times as great as it is for an electron,[7] hence the uncertainty is a billion times smaller. Even if we assume again that $\Delta x = 10^{-8}$ cm, we find $\Delta v = 1$ millimeter per sec. But for something as large as a cell it is unreasonable to allow Δx so small a value, which is far beyond the limit of detection. If we increase it 1,000-fold, the indeterminacy in velocity goes down to 10^{-3} mm/sec, a value so small as to be quite uninteresting.

But this argument is really no more cogent than the former. For one might well ask: who is interested in the motion of a brain cell, or a neuron as a whole? It is very likely that crucial processes within such miniature organisms are triggered by single electrons and photons which *are* very strongly affected by quantum mechanical indeterminacy. Although little is known about the details of these reactions there is a good deal of conclusive evidence to support the claim that quantum indeterminacy can project important effects into the world at large, that organisms, in particular, can have their behavior and their fate strongly influenced by interaction with elementary physical entities. Again observe: even if we succeed in showing this we are still far from having established freedom. I am not suggesting that the release of erratic behavior governed only by the laws of chance is tantamount to freedom. I am saying that it is a physical precondition for human freedom. As to the influence of atomic chance upon the macroworld, here are a few examples.

Meteorology is not an exact science, and I am particularly reluctant to draw upon it because my knowledge of it is most inadequate. Everyone knows, however, that large atmospheric disturbances spring from minute pressure and velocity changes taking place within small regions in the upper air. A few molecules with abnormally large velocities can trigger a movement which may develop into a cyclone. I had always thought that the nucleus of a large disturbance would have to contain a sizeable number of molecules. However, a distinguished meteorologist recently told me that a fluctuation in velocity no larger than is compatible with Heisenberg's principle can be the cause of a low. And on looking at the mathematics, I convinced myself of this possibility. Only the probability of its happening is extremely small.

Scientists working in the psychophysics of vision have shown that a receptor in the human retina is sensitive to the incidence of very few photons of light, in certain regions of the spectrum perhaps to a single one. This means that a conscious response can be elicited by physical entities whose behavior is controlled by the uncertainty principle, a response which is in the customary sense without original cause. To be sure, it was triggered by the impinging photons, hence there was an immediate cause. But the coming of the photons was unpredictable; therefore the ensuing sensation, the stimulus-response episode was causeless. Yet that sensation might have informed a subject in a dark night that "something was there", perhaps something threatening, and he could have taken measures to avert the danger.

A more impressive illustration of the intrusion of atomic chance into the living world is afforded by the mutation of genes, which is known to result sometimes from the impact of a single X-ray quantum. Such mutations can be advantageous to the individual undergoing them, but more often they are debilitating, sometimes lethal. A documented example is found in the literature.[8] It is impressive because it affected the fate of nations. It is well known that hemophilia, the bleeding disease, was an affliction of the ruling families of Russia and of Spain ever since the middle of the 19th century, troublesome in politics and a threat to royal succession. The origin of this disease may well be hidden in the indeterministic realm of atomic processes. Haldane has suggested after considerable search that the hemophilic condition began with a gene mutation in the nucleus of a cell in one of the testicles of Edward, Duke of Kent, Queen Victoria's father, in the year 1818.

From there on the incidence of the disease is open to study. There were three hemophiliacs among Victoria's nine children, seven among her grandchildren, six in the fourth generation. The latter included Alexis, the crown prince of Russia, whose mother, neurotically anxious about his condition, sought help from the monk Rasputin. How he thus gained a fateful foothold in the affairs of the Czarist family is a matter of history. Hemophilia among the sons of Alphonso XIII, the King of Spain, who was a grandson of Queen Victoria, apparently affected the stability of the throne.

Clearly, it is difficult to maintain that atomic indeterminacy has nothing to do with the inhabitants of the macrocosm.

Having made this point, I now turn to a

few logical arguments which have been levelled against the possibility of freedom, quite apart from physical indeterminacy. Professor J. J. C. Smart[9] has attempted to dispose of freedom as an inconsistent concept by employing a simple and seemingly cogent logical argument. He constructs two theses which he assumes to be exhaustive of all possibilities and also mutually exclusive. One is Laplacian determinism as we have discussed it earlier, the other is the view that "there are some events that even a superhuman calculator could not predict, however precise his knowledge of however wide a region of the universe at some previous time." Freedom, he holds, violates both of them and is therefore ruled out.

Certainly the requirement of impeccable logic is to be imposed on every phase of scientific and philosophic reasoning; nevertheless logic, in spite of its merited vogue, is not the sole arbiter of truth. There are instances where the diffuseness of the meaning of terms makes its formal application impossible and its conclusions spurious in spite of all the reverence it commands. In the present instance, its use to settle the argument concerning freedom is as ineffectual as the application of arithmetic to ideas.

Smart's algorithm was challenged neatly by Harris,[10] who rightly insists that the two alternatives above are *not* mutually exclusive. If freedom were identical with Smart's second alternative we would call it erratic behavior or caprice. What makes Harris' point important is, first of all, the looseness which afflicts the term event (state, or observation, or measurement would be more acceptable), and second the fact that physical indeterminacy is precisely the kind of intermediate alternative which is neither coincident with Smart's proposition one nor with proposition two.

One of the most serious confusions about freedom arises in connection with the uniqueness of history. The course of events in the universe is a single flow; there is no ambiguity about the happenings at any given time, aside from our knowledge of them, and if a superhuman intellect knew everything that happened up to a certain time T, he would perceive, in looking backward, not only clear determinism but a rigid, filled space-time structure of events. He could in fact, if he were a mathematician, write a formula— with a proper qualitative text defining the nature of all events—which would represent all history up to T. Where, then, can freedom enter in the presence of that timeless formula which, although it was unknown at times before T, nevertheless "existed" in a mathematical sense?

The answer involves recognition of the fact that retrodiction is not the same as prediction. Indeterminacy permits the former but not the latter. Only Laplacian determinism makes inferences along the time axis symmetric in both directions. On classical mechanics, full knowledge of the state of a physical system at time T allows in principle the calculation of its state at any time before or after T. Indeterminacy introduces a peculiar asymmetry into states with respect to their temporal implications: the past is certain and the future is not. This causal irreversibility of time is, and must always be, asserted along with the affirmation of freedom.

Nor is this without consequences with respect to the nature of time. The recent controversy concerning emergence or becoming, and the sense in which time is a fourth dimension of space[11] is strongly affected by it. Relativity theory, which is thus far an outgrowth of classical mechanics and does not incorporate indeterminacy, speaks in Laplace's voice and precludes creativity and emergence of features not already foreshadowed in the presence. In the controversy to which reference has just been made, Capec is right in arguing for emergence, not for any philosophic reason but for the simple scien-

tific fact that ordinary 4-dimensional relativity, the basis for the claim of frozen passage, is not applicable to the atomic domain.

Having reviewed the most common objections met by those who affirm human freedom, and having attempted to expose their
weaknesses, let me now summarize and state
my case.

Classical determinism made freedom intrinsically impossible, unless its application
to psycho-physical phenomena is arbitrarily
interdicted.

Historic arguments designed to reconcile
freedom with classical causality were able
merely to establish a subjective illusion, a
personal feeling of freedom.

Modern physics, through Heisenberg's
principle of indeterminacy, has loosened Laplacian determinism sufficiently to allow *un-
caused* atomic events, permitting in certain
specifiable situations the incidence of genuine
chance.

The consequence of such microcosmic indeterminacies, while usually insignificant in the molar world, do ingress into the macrocosm at least in several known instances. It is very likely that they play a role in delicate neuro-physical and chemical processes.

Physics thus makes understandable the occurrence of *chance*, of true alternatives upon which the course of events must seize. Physics alone, in its present state, can account for unpredictable, erratic human behavior.

Human freedom involves more than chance: it joins chance with deliberate *choice*. But it needs the chance. In so far, and so long, as science can say nothing about this latter active, decisive, creative element it has not fully solved the problem of freedom.

But it has lifted it out of the wastebasket of illusions and paradoxes and re-established it as a challenging problem to be further resolved.

And now an afterthought. Suppose physical science, perhaps with the aid of sister disciplines like psychology, philosophy and theology, had solved the problem of choice super-vening upon chance to explain freedom, would this fuller understanding not restore determinism? If we can *explain* how the agency effecting choice selects from the alternatives presented by physics a particular one, will the inclusion of that agency into the scheme of things not leave us where we started, i.e. with an amplified Laplacian formula?

The answer cannot be forseen. It may be affirmative, but I strongly doubt it. For if that agency were one which looked into the future rather than into the past, were drawn by purposes rather than impelled by drives, partook of the liveliness of the incalculable human spirit—freedom in a unique sense would survive.

APPENDIX

SCIENCE AND ETHICS

Scientists have often claimed that scientific knowledge itself, when fully grasped, will generate the rules of proper human conduct. Beginning with Socrates' doctrine that knowledge is virtue they have endeavored through the ages to squeeze the *is*, hoping that it would yield an *ought*. The futility of such an undertaking needs to be unmasked and clearly exposed to view; for it involves the naturalistic fallacy which has been rightly criticised by many writers. To put it simply: even if we knew everything about the physical universe, about human physiology, about man's natural dispositions, his drives, his instincts and his normal reaction to all stimuli; even if we could predict how average men will in scientific fact behave under all specified circumstances (at a given time of the evolutionary process), we should still have no basis for judging the moral quality of his actions. Even if the drive for survival or for individual happiness were absolutely universal we could still not prove, by using the laws of science, that man *ought* not to die or *ought* to be unhappy in certain situations. This absence of affinity between the substance of science and the substance of ethics must be recognized at the outset. Although I shall suggest in the sequel that we are in possession of principles which may, if properly applied, engender facilities for judging objectively the moral behavior of men, and to judge them independently of local standards of value, I do not refer to *any generalizations of scientific fact*.

I am, however, suggesting that the abstract methodology of science, which enables us to rise from particular fact to universal law, contains important hints relating to the possible conversion of the factual moral *is* into the regulative *ought*, to the transformation of values conceived culturally and relatively, into values embodying transcultural norms. Before presenting the details of this suggestion it seems desirable, for the sake of clear communication, to analyze the semantics of the word value.

1. The Meaning of Value

Traditionally, the center of attention among moral philosophers is the concept of *value*. Human actions are said to strive towards the acquisition, or attainment, or realization of "values," and the hope is held out that if values can only be classified according to some reliable principles or measured on some universal scale, then the moral quality of an action can at once be determined by the kind or the loftiness of the value which the action intends to realize. Such a procedure is suggested, albeit without clear promise of success, by the simpler natural sciences to which the advocates of this theory of value often refer.

SCIENTIFIC INDETERMINISM

However, in actual fact science offers neither support nor refutation of the thesis that human actions refer to a scale of values and that values are measurably correlated with some property engendered by or accompanying actions. The thesis must therefore be subjected to logical scrutiny and to the test of factual success. It could fail because the concept, value, might *not* be capable of sufficiently precise definition, might *not* be referrable to any unique scale; or values may not be the purposes (or the causes) of human action; or the chosen scale itself might prove unreliable. It is my belief that all these misadventures have occurred and are secretly troubling those who travel into ethics through the theory of values; that the concept of value itself is at present the object of a global rescue operation involving most of the resources of what is traditionally called moral philosophy.

Another kind of question can be asked concerning values. Quite apart from any success or failure of the attempt to assign value to actions and then measure value by reference to some other perhaps more easily discernible quality, one needs also to make sure that this correspondence when established is sufficient to complete the task of ethics, which is to set *normative*, not merely de facto standards of conduct. It is conceivable, for example, that it could satisfy the scientific query as to what men do, how they in fact behave, but leave unanswered the question whether it is right or wrong that they should thus behave. In that case the theory of values might serve as a basis for cultural anthropology and for sociology, but not for a kind of ethics which requires a standard of judgment higher than observed behavior.

Let us consider briefly the current meanings of the word value. Since that word is so often called upon to perform important service, it may be well to review its linguistic origin. Somehow, our comprehension of things, situations and people tends to be deepened, our interest in them quickened by a knowledge of their ancestral histories, and this should certainly be true for words like value that are employed as pack animals. In this instance, we discover an interesting variety of meanings among its ancestors, only one of which—and not the primary meaning—has come to be reflected in the present usage of the word.

The Latin *valere*, from which value is derived, meant primarily to enjoy physical strength. The adjective *validus* is frequently applied to a bull (taurus validus). But the word took on related meanings: to be capable in a more general sense, to be powerful, influential. The state of health was always included in its Latin connotation, as is evident in the Roman farewell: *vale*. The metaphoric extension goes on from "powerful" to "fitting" and "appropriate" and finally to the notion of equivalence" of coins ("dum pro argenteis decem aureus unus valeret"). Here the original comes close to our present usage, as when we speak of the equi*valence* of words. For in Latin, synonyms are words of "equal value" ("verbum, quod idem valeat") . Rarely, however, would the Roman have used valere to refer to value in our present primary sense; this would have been more accurately rendered by *pretium*, *honos*, or *virtus*.

Interestingly, if value has been upgraded from physical strength to general worth, the word "price" has suffered the opposite fate. It started approximately where value ended, with the Latin *pretio*, and has now come down to its mundane usage in economics. The French *prix* and the Spanish *precio* still retain a little of the more "precious" flavor.

We now inspect the meanings of value in today's context. Simple words implying value judgments are good, pleasant, beautiful, genuine, honorable, virtuous, and their opposites. They can be applied to several different types of noun, those denoting things, persons and indeed processes or courses of action. For the present we restrict our discussion to things and persons. One peculiar aspect about the assignment of a value to an object, often noted in the literature and greatly emphasized by G. E. Moore,[12] is its indirectness of reference. When we say an object is good we do not mean it is blue, large, heavy or that it possesses any other particular sensory qualities; yet in another sense we mean all of these. Goodness is not a natural property of objects but still it expresses itself *through* their natural properties. For this reason, goodness, and more generally value, are often termed non-natural qualities of things. Here then arises one of the much discussed problems of value theory: are non-natural qualities reducible to natural ones; are they a collective function of all the natural qualities of an object; do they refer to something aside from the natural qualities such as the reaction of a human mind or the use to which the object can be put; or are non-natural qualities irreducible and *sui generis*? The last proposition is affirmed by Moore.

The present approach to values and ethics lies in a different direction, for we are less interested in the logic of usages than in the dynamics of ethical procedures. Let us therefore abandon the study of values as non-natural qualities of things.

Values are properties or attributes of *things*. They attach, first of all, to concrete objects. Here, value is generated by the use to which they can be put, and this use is either a limited one in the status of loan or lease, or it is unlimited in outright ownership.

Values are also attributed to *intangibles* like health, happiness, friendship, security and leisure. Different principles begin to operate here, primarily because one of the components which determine the value of commodities ceases to be significant; these intangibles can be created at will, they are not subject to laws of material supply and thus indefinitely available. Hence these intangible goods defy the laws of arithmetic, which are applicable only to discrete things. We have no calculus suitable for an assignment of value in these instances. They are, at least at present, unmeasurable and are for that reason often called *qualities* in contradistinction to *quantities*.

Hence other, less precise and more intuitive means are forced upon us in the endeavor to appraise such things as health, love and happiness. One possibility is to select arbitrarily one of them, say happiness, as primary, and then judge the competence of others, such as health and love to create this primary good. I used the word "arbitrarily" with deliberation for I know of no rigorous criterion that would accent one "good" more heavily than another. Attempts go forth in many places to show that there is indeed a primary good, definable in more basic terms, such as human self-fulfilment, or the goal of human evolution or the survival of the race. All of these "more basic" principles, it seems to me, are forced to beg the final question as to why they should be regarded as good at all.

It is utterly astonishing to see how many moral philosophers, though rigorously trained in logic, and often exclusively in logic, persistently balk at the need for *choice* which confronts us here. One of the deepest insights conveyed to us by this branch of modern philosophy concerns the impossibility of establishing a formal system that is assuredly self-consistent and complete, and certainly none that can do without chosen axioms and primitives. It should be evident, therefore, that at some place one must meet a legitimate occasion for arbitrary choice, and apparently we have met one here.

AND HUMAN FREEDOM

We thus conclude that the value of intangibles is estimated intuitively by the degree to which they contribute to the creation or maintenance of some primitively defined and wisely chosen "absolute" or primary good.

The preceding comments dealt first with the value of common objects, limited and unlimited in their availability, and secondly with the value of intangibles. At the next stage we encounter living creatures and we ask about *their* value. Life itself, of course, has value, but it belongs to the former class of intangibles. One might attempt to make the transition from there to the value of living things by imparting to the latter simply the value of life; but this clearly fails, for then all living creatures would have equal value. Nor will the addition of other intangibles beside life yield a measure of value: when one speaks of a good person his goodness is clearly not meant to be a function of his perceptible qualities or of the intangibles with which he is endowed. A happy mood does not make him good, neither will health, nor love of his parents or his fellowmen. These do not constitute his goodness even though they may be a necessary condition for it. No, the goodness of a person is clearly dependent on what he *does*. An important change is thus seen to occur as we pass from the study of value in inanimate objects or in abstract qualities to the domain of the living, where "free" decision is possible together with voluntary action. It is through the accident of freedom that the meaning of good, and indeed of the entire value concept, is transferred from its lodgings in external qualities—where it resides for things—to the internal dynamics of willing and acting. A person is good because *what he does is in accord with certain rules*.

In the shift to the living, then, we have made the transition to ethics. A good egg and a good boy are incomparably different in the connotations of good. Having encountered and recognized what constitutes value in man, we have likewise uncovered the main springs of ethics: will and action in accordance with certain rules.

We have dealt with the nature of values and the ways by which they are established and made manifest. Each value, however, when established, still prompts us to ask whether indeed it *ought* to be a value and, if it is, whether our assessment of it is "right." A fact is what it is and must be accepted as such; its essence is fulfilled in its being, not in its being right or wrong. Values, on the other hand, have both a factual and a normative component, the latter declaring itself in the judgment of an ought.

We encounter the second component along with the first on all levels of valuation. A thing may be valued or priced in accordance with custom, subjective want or the laws of supply and demand. Its factual value is thus fixed. Nonetheless we wonder whether the value or the price is *right*.

As one moves to higher planes of value, the problem

of the ought presents itself with greater urgency and at the same time, as if in compensation, the area of dispute concerning it is lessened. Life, health, honesty are all acclaimed as desirable in the overriding judgment of most men. Little need therefore be said here about the normative aspects of intangible values.

It is on the third level, in the vast arena of human actions, that the ought becomes imperative. And precisely there the distinction between the factual and the normative is widely disregarded. Value in the social sciences is too frequently identified with the actual behavior, with observed preferences of people within a group, and this is then often tacitly elevated to a norm. The reason for this oversimplified treatment of social situations is easy to see: preferences are observable, statistically measurable while norms are not, and the view prevails that what is measurable becomes ipso facto scientific, and everybody wants sociology to be a science. Nevertheless, when common practice is accepted as normative, the ideas of obligation, honor, guilt, remorse and retribution undergo an erosion which transforms them into shallow psychological phenomena, and leaves their human victims at the mercy of psychiatrists.

There is what one might call a scale of oughts. This phrase is intended to convey, first that the normative note rings audibly in every value judgment, and second, that its intensity rises in a crescendo from mere detectability in the assignment of material values to imperative urgency in valuating human actions. In the sequel, when the word value carries its accent on the factual, as in comparative anthropology, I shall call it an "est value"; when its meaning is normative, super-factual, I shall use the term "esto-value." The important question then is: how can esto values be objectively established? The easy way, which involves reliance upon revealed doctrinal truth, is evidently not open to people and societies which reject such truth. We therefore look for an alternate, perhaps a complementary method of establishing esto values by both formal and empirical means.

2. The Parallelism Between Science and Ethics Viewed as Empirical Enterprises

This section is intended to show that, while ethics and science are completely different in their substances (what ought to be vs. what is) and their languages (imperative vs. indicative), their abstract methodologies are similar. This similarity can be used to clarify many problems of traditional ethics.

For the sake of brevity, let me explain the relevant aspects of the scientific method, conceived in its widest generality, by means of a simplifying diagram. An extended discussion of it is given in *The Nature of Physical Reality*.[13] In figure 1 are depicted symbolically various stages of the process by which scientific knowledge is acquired and verified. At the top we encounter the level of protocol experiences, the sense data, the observa-

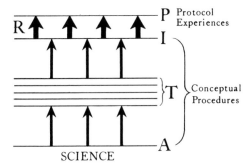

tions which, being incoherent and devoid of order in themselves, require "explanations" and rationalization by supplementary concepts which are not directly given in the protocol domain. Explanation involves conceptual procedures, schematically outlined in the figure by the structure of levels below the protocol experiences. They function in the following way.

At the base every science exhibits very general propositions called axioms and denoted by A. These axioms differ in the different sciences; only occasionally, when branches of inquiry attain a very high degree of development, do their bases coalesce. This happened, for example, in certain parts of physics and chemistry when quantum mechanics was discovered. Whatever the axioms of a given science (or of a part of science) at a given time may be, they give rise by deductive formal explication to higher level, i.e. less general propositions which are ordinarily called laws or theorems and are designated by T in the diagram. From the various T one derives still more particular inferences, called I in figure 1. For instance in geometry A might represent the axioms of Euclid, T the various theorems about plane figures, I statements about the properties of right triangles such as Pythagoras' theorem. These final inferences are in general still devoid of empirical content, since they refer to formal elements which have no necessary counterpart in the world of sense, that is, among protocol experiences. Indeed the entire range of conceptual procedures from A to I represents a formal system, of interest to the logician and the mathematician. To convert it into an applied science one must place it into correspondence with the P-plane of the diagram, and this requires the introduction of a set of relations, labelled R, which permit I to be compared with P.

In some sciences, (e.g. geometry) the propositions composing I speak of sides of triangles, angles, lengths of lines which immediately suggest comparison with actual observable objects. In others the connection is very remote. For instance, a great deal of analysis and insight was required before Max Born recognized that the simple construct ψ, which appears as the solution of the Schrodinger equation, has reference to a probability distribution of observations in the protocol domain. A special set of *rules* stating that relation had to be discovered, a set called "rules of correspondence"; these are designated by R in figure 1. Closer inspection reveals that every science requires rules of correspondence, although their presence has long gone undetected. This is true even in geometry; for the lines and angles of an ideal triangle, which is the object of the conceptual procedures, are not truly identical with the elements of concrete figures drawn on material blackboards. Nor is the temperature, which functions as an abstract symbol in the propositions concerning heat phenomena, propositions which flow ultimately from the axioms of thermodynamics, recognizable as in any sense identical with the indication of a material thermometer. The two are related by an operational definition, as explained in ref. 1, and that operational definition, like the other connecting links just mentioned, is what I have called a rule of correspondence.

It is by virtue of these rules that the conceptual procedures can be brought into contact with P-experiences; through them, scientific verification of theories becomes possible.

Thus far, our attention has been confined to the description of the connections between various levels of our diagram. Let us now raise the question of *entailment*. Clearly, when A is given we can rise without injection of further postulates to the level I. The conceptual procedures are more or less self-contained. But to go from I to P we need the rules of correspondence, and these are not entailed by what is below or what is above them. They are *chosen*, much as one chooses axioms, with an eye upon how the entire scheme of explanation is most likely to work successfully. The gap between I and P is a logical hiatus which a special postulational fiat must bridge.

The axioms, of course, are likewise unentailed; they are subject to human choice. Again, this was not clearly understood in earlier periods of science, when axioms were regarded as ultimate, unchangeable truths. We now know that they do change as science develops, and that their flexibility imparts to science the dynamism, the self-corrective qualities which are so generally admired and which a static basis can not provide.

We conclude our survey of the method of science by emphasizing once more the postulational character of two elements or levels in figure 1: A and R. If scientists were not free to choose these important elements of their method, or if they entertained major disagreements concerning them, their enterprise could not be successful: it would probably be in the same state as current theories of value.

Having studied the methodology or, in a large sense, the fundamental language of science, we now examine the language of values with special reference to human actions. I propose to develop that language by means of a diagram very similar to figure 1. Our basic concern shifts from the goal of *explanation* to the goal of *suasive control of human actions*, from a descriptive

analysis of what happens to a hortative language of
how men ought to act. In view of this shift the gram-
matical form of all relevant statements must be altered.
Whereas the basis of figure 1, A, contained declarative
sentences, the basis of figure 2 depicting the methodology of ethics speaks in imperatives or command-

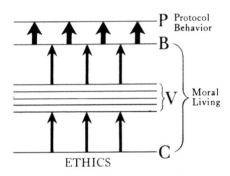

FIGURE 2

ments, *C*. To be sure, other starting points of ethics
have at times been proposed by philosophers, but the
testimony of history demonstrates impressively, I think,
that all effective moral philosophies have begun with
imperatives. The commands, C, *imply* specific rules of
conduct, propositions relating to particular human
situations. Thus, the commandment "thou shalt not
kill" entails that one should preserve life; hence human
life becomes a value. If "thou shalt not steal" is in-

cluded in V, *property* becomes a value. For this reason I have labelled such deductive consequences V, for value, in figure 2. But I would rather not regard V as a *logical* explication of C since I do not look upon logic as the primary determinant of ethical systems: V follows from C through the process of *living*; a social group dedicated to C evolves values, not by speculation but by concrete actions. In further detail this living process engenders particular patterns of behavior, B. The ethical enterprise from the basis C to its vital implications B is therefore continuous, but this continuity ends at B.

Science became an empirical, verifiable system of reasoning because the rules of correspondence permitted a confrontation of the level I with protocol experiences. Their absence would have left science without application, like some parts of pure mathematics. In a similar way, ethics remains unverifiable, devoid of universal oughts if analysis is forced to stop at B. The behavior B itself satisfies no criterion of external validation, for it follows from C and can therefore not be used to validate C. The passage from C to B is "vitally tautological," that is to say, a given group of people, a culture, living in accordance with C will automatically exhibit a behavior pattern labelled B. How, then, do we get from B to the level above, called protocol behavior? What is this ethical protocol, and what are the rules of correspondence joining it with B?

Many moral philosophers, especially in occidental cultures, have tried to develop systems of ethics from postulates concerning human goals. Eudemonism, hedonism, utilitarianism are names of such attempts. The telling characteristic of all these endeavors is that by themselves they remain ineffective. A living ethical system has never come out of any proposition which merely records that man's goal is happiness. That knowledge is simply not sufficient to guide man's action in specific circumstances. But if a principle claiming that happiness is man's desirable goal were placed on top of the elements composing that part of figure 2 called "Moral Living," if it were used as a *criterion of validity* for the actually occurring level B, the ethical enterprise could be satisfactorily completed. The empirical facts of B could then be compared with the ideal protocol behavior *defined* by the principle of happiness.

For this reason I am loathe to accept eudemonism and all the other human goals which have been offered as *the* basic principles of ethics. They are principles in terms of which chosen sets of imperatives can be validated. I therefore prefer to call them principles of validation, or postulated *primary* values (in contradistinction to the values V which automatically result from the commands). If this understanding is accepted, figure 2 takes on a remarkable similarity to figure 1. The primary values function in a role comparable with the rules of correspondence, enabling comparison be-between B and P. There are differences, to be sure, but their discussion will be omitted in this concentrated account.

SCIENTIFIC INDETERMINISM

The scientific process is successful when I agrees with P in figure 1. The ethical process is successful when B agrees with P in figure 2. In the former case, scientific theory is verified; in the latter, ethical norms are validated. Before verification scientific constructs form hypotheses, afterwards they become true, confirmed theories or laws which state universal (though not ultimate) truth. Before validation, ethical imperatives are tentative, reflect local patterns of behavior and make no universal normative pretensions; after validation they transcend the est and take on the esto character of an ought.

Scholars versed primarily in the humanities tend to regard the theory I have proposed as unsatisfactory because it leaves the origin of the commands as well as the origin of the principles of validation obscure and the principles themselves subject to human choice. To me this is encouraging, since it reflects precisely the epistemological status of the axioms and the rules of correspondence in the scientific scheme. Indeed it increases my hope that the ethical enterprise can be successful inasmuch as it involves all those ingredients which have made science successful within its realm. And I am further delighted that it gives man choices instead of a rigid and immutable structure of norms.

Let us also note the strong affinity between ethics and religion. If ethics has the methodological structure here outlined, then it is open ended like every other human enterprise. Postulates (the Commandments) form its base, and other postulates (principles of validation or primary values) enter near the summit. It is but natural for man to regard their injection into the stream of history by blessed individuals as acts of revelation. It is here that ethics and religion come together.

3. On The Possibility of Transcultural Ethical Norms

In the preceding section we surveyed the infelicitous and hopeless state of a language which talks about values per se. Values are not useful starting points of any discussion that aims to deal with human behavior in terms which claim relevance for the total multicultural panorama. As our diagram shows, they are situated in the middle between the imperatives and the validated behavior (figure 2); they draw their meaning from C, their authority and their ought from the agreement between B and P.

Perhaps we can now see the reason why international communication about values has been blocked. Values as ordinarily conceived make no reference to the methodology of science, indeed they spurn it by a pretense of aloofness which arrogantly disclaims all connections between value and fact. Hence those who place their entire trust in the language of science are repelled by such talk about values; in particular they see no opportunities for meaningful comparisons of different cultural standards. In the context here developed, values are the counterparts of the tested laws of science and their claim for consideration can become tempestuous among those who insist on speaking the scientific and no other tongue. There is a chance, at least, that this new view of ethics, which converts that ancient branch of philosophy into an empirical and a challenging undertaking, will restore communication about values between scholars in alien ideologies.

NOTES

1. In a fundamental sense there is no difference between elementary particles and waves. These ultimates are neither; they defy such simple description. Nor can we be sure that they are elementary. The term I like to apply to them is the noncommittal Greek "onta".

2. H. Margenau, *The Nature of Physical Reality* (New York: McGraw Hill Co., 1950).

3. Margenau, *The Nature of Physical Reality*.

4. If the forms of $W(x)$ and $W(p)$ are different, Δx and Δp have slightly different meanings.

5. H. Margenau, *Ethics and Science* (Princeton: D. Van Nostrand Co., 1964).

6. Perhaps one ought to weigh here the possibility that this awareness is illusive, like the experience of an

hallucination. Both, awareness of freedom and hallucinations are, of course, subjective. But so are the colors
I see; indeed every science starts with subjective protocol experiences. Hence subjectivity is no ground for
rejecting either. The characteristic features of an hallucination are two. First, it defies repetition under prearranged circumstances; second, it defies physical explanation. The conjunction of these two attributes calls
for scientific rejection. Awareness of free choice can be
indefinitely repeated under easily contrived circumstances, for it occurs whenever we are given an alternative and act deliberately. It is certainly as real and
regular as the pain I feel when I injure my body. What
it fails to satisfy is the expectation that it should have
a physical explanation. This, however, is true of many
events which are presumed to be real. Indeed most
interesting experiences lack explanations when they
first occur. But freedom as a direct experience is in a
better condition with respect to being understood than
many other phenomena. For as will be shown we *can*
see how it is possible, though not as yet how it works
scientifically.

6a. Some evidence that this may be the case is already
visible though not conclusive. There is a peculiar
phenomenon called turbulence, an erratic, often unstable state of a fluid medium, which can only be
described and analyzed by statistical methods. These
methods disallow the prediction of the exact dynamical
state of the fluid at a future time, and it is believed

by competent investigators the turbulent media do not have unique futures, that they are causally indeterminate *macro*scopic states subject to intrinsic indeterminacies much of the Heisenberg type. If this is true we are already facing an enlargement of the issues here reviewed, and we glimpse perhaps attractive possibilities of relating physiological conditions in brain cells which are akin to turbulence with physically non-unique futures of organisms.

7. A synaptic knob within the cerebral cortex weighs 5×10^{-13} gm, i.e. 10^{14} times as much as an electron. J. C. Eccles, (*The Neurophysiological Basis of Mind*, Oxford, 1953) considers the possibility that particles within these knobs, free under physical indeterminacy, may have their behavior influenced by the mind.

8. J. R. S. Haldane, *"Royal Blood," The Living Age 356* (1939), p. 26.

9. *Mind* (1961), Vol. LXX.

10. E. Harris, *Foundations of Metaphysics in Science* (New York: Allen and Unwin Ltd. 1965).

11. D. Williams, "The Myth of Frozen Passage," *Journal of Philosophy of Science* (1966), *48*, 457; M. Capec, *Boston Studies in Philosophy of Science* (1966), II, 441.

12. G. E. Moore, *Principia Ethica* (Oxford University Press, 1912).

13. H. Margenau, 1950.

Errata

Page seven, line 19, *read:* point), and the . . .

Page twenty-seven, line 2, *read:* be established after numerous trials.

Page thirty, line 15, *read:* the Laplacian form.

Page thirty-seven, line 5, *read:* . . . elsewhere.[3]

Page forty-eight, line 5, *read:* . . . atomic entity . . .

Page fifty-nine, line 8, *read:* self free to move . . .